HOUGHTON MIFFLIN
The Literature Experience
READING

Celebrate Reading with us!

ISBN: 0-395-61079-6

23456789-D-96 95 94 93

Too Big

Senior Author
John J. Pikulski

*Senior Coordinating
Author*
J. David Cooper

*Senior Consulting
Author*
William K. Durr

Coordinating Authors
Kathryn H. Au
M. Jean Greenlaw
Marjorie Y. Lipson
Susan E. Page
Sheila W. Valencia
Karen K. Wixson

Authors
Rosalinda B. Barrera
Edwina Bradley
Ruth P. Bunyan
Jacqueline L. Chaparro
Jacqueline C. Comas
Alan N. Crawford
Robert L. Hillerich
Timothy G. Johnson
Jana M. Mason
Pamela A. Mason
William E. Nagy
Joseph S. Renzulli
Alfredo Schifini

Senior Advisor
Richard C. Anderson

Advisors
Christopher J. Baker
Charles Peters
MaryEllen Vogt

HOUGHTON MIFFLIN COMPANY   BOSTON
Atlanta   Dallas   Geneva, Illinois   Palo Alto   Princeton   Toronto

🎖 Award Winner

Animal

Animal friends are everywhere! Not just in zoos, forests, and pet shops—but in books, too. You will read about many animal friends in these stories and poems. Here come the animals!

Friends

9

BIG BOOK

Skip to My Lou
adapted and illustrated by
Nadine Bernard Westcott

This book is about a boy who lives on a farm. When the farmer and his wife go out, some animal friends come into the house!
Read this book together and sing the words as a song. Find out if the animals can help the boy clean the house by two o'clock!

Who Is Tapping

by A. G. Deming
pictures by Monica Wellington

At My Window?

Who is tapping at my window?

"It's not I," said the cat.

"It's not I," said the rat.

"It's not I," said the wren.

"It's not I," said the hen.

"It's not I," said the fox.

"It's not I," said the ox.

"It's not I," said the loon.

"It's not I," said the raccoon.

"It's not I," said the cony.

"It's not I," said the pony.

"It's not I," said the dog.

"It's not I," said the frog.

"It's not I," said the bear.

"It's not I," said the hare.

Who is tapping at my window?

"It is I," said the rain,

"tapping at your windowpane."

Animal Pictures

You have just read about some animal friends. Which one did you like best? Where could this animal go when it rains?

Draw a picture to show where the animal might go.

Meet the ILLUSTRATOR

Monica Wellington has always loved to draw. She went to art school to study drawing. One day, Ms. Wellington was reading a very old poetry book. She found A. G. Deming's poem "Who Is Tapping At My Window?" She liked the poem so much that she drew pictures for it and made it into a storybook.

Morning on the Farm

A Traditional Song · illustrated by Felicia Bond

When sheep get up in the morning,
They always say, "Good day."

When sheep get up in the morning,
They always say, "Good day."

"Baa, baa, baa, baa,"
That is what they say, they say.

"Baa, baa, baa, baa,"
That is what they say.

31

When dogs get up in the morning,
They always say, "Good day."

When dogs get up in the morning,
They always say, "Good day."

"Bow–wow–wow–wow,"
That is what they say, they say.

"Bow–wow–wow–wow,"
That is what they say.

When ducks get up in the morning,
They always say, "Good day."

When ducks get up in the morning,
They always say, "Good day."

"Quack, quack! Quack, quack!"
That is what they say, they say.

"Quack, quack! Quack, quack!"
That is what they say.

33

When frogs get up in the morning,
They always say, "Good day."

When frogs get up in the morning,
They always say, "Good day."

"Rib–bet, rib–bet,"
That is what they say, they say.

"Rib–bet, rib–bet,"
That is what they say.

Early Morning

a traditional poem,
translated from the Spanish

Like a ringing alarm clock,
My grandmother wakes me.
"Time to go to school, dear!"
She says as she shakes me.

And the horse says neigh!
The bull says moo!
The frog says ribbit!
The cat says mew!
The dog says arf!
The sheep says baa!
The hen says cluck!
The goat says maa!
The donkey says heehaw!
The pig says squeee!
And the rooster sings out:
Kee-kee-ree-kee!

The sky starts to clear,
The sun starts to peep,
And with all that singing,
I CAN'T SLEEP!

Dear Zoo

Rod Campbell

I wrote to the zoo

to send me a pet.

They sent me an...

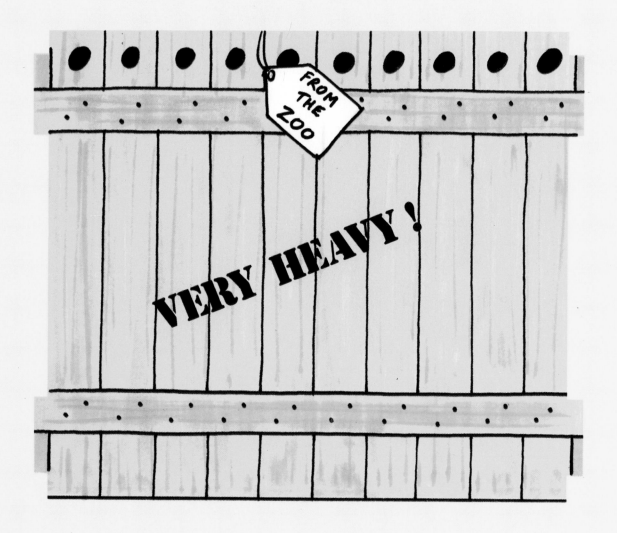

He was too big!
I sent him back.

So they sent me a...

fragile

He was too tall!
I sent him back.

So they sent me a ...

He was too fierce!
I sent him back.

So they sent me a ...

He was too grumpy!
I sent him back.

So they sent me a ...

He was too scary!
I sent him back.

So they sent me a ...

He was too naughty!
I sent him back.

So they sent me a ...

He was too jumpy!
I sent him back.

So they thought
very hard, and
sent me a ...

He was perfect!

I kept him.

Write a Letter

Do you think the zoo animals in the story would make good pets? Why or why not?

Think of an animal you would like for a pet. Then write a letter to a zoo, a farm, or a pet shop. Ask them to send you the animal.

Draw a picture to show why you would like to have this animal as a pet.

Dear Farm,

I want a pet. Please send me a chicken. Thank you. Yours truly, Jessica

Author and Illustrator

Rod Campbell grew up in Africa. There, he saw many jungle animals. He wrote about those animals in *Dear Zoo*. He also drew the pictures for the book.

Mr. Campbell now lives in London, England.

At the Zoo

I've been to the zoo
   where the thing that you do
is watching the things
   that the animals do —

and watching
   the animals
   all watching
    you!

by Myra Cohn Livingston

Poems About Animal Friends

THE LOST CAT

We can't find the cat,

We don't know where she's at,

Oh, where did she go?

Does anyone know?

Let's ask this walking hat.

by Shel Silverstein

NOTICE

I have a dog,
I had a cat.
I've got a frog
Inside my hat.

by David McCord

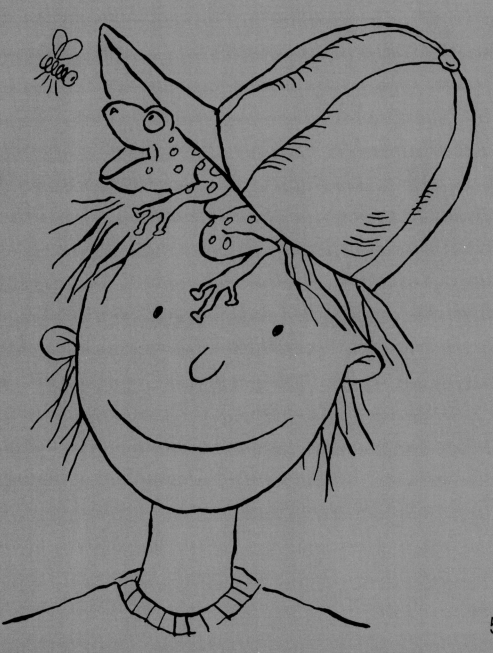

GOMI TARO.

My Friends

by Taro Gomi

I learned to walk from my friend the cat.

I learned to jump from my friend the dog.

I learned to climb from my friend
the monkey.

I learned to run from my friend the horse.

I learned to march from my friend
the rooster.

I learned to nap from

my friend the crocodile.

I learned to smell the flowers from
my friend the butterfly.

I learned to hide from
my friend the rabbit.

I learned to explore the earth from

my friend the ant.

I learned to kick from my friend
the gorilla.

I learned to watch the night sky
from my friend the owl.

I learned to sing from my friends the birds.

I learned to read from
my friends the books.

I learned to study from
      my friends the teachers.

I learned to play from
      my friends at school.

And I learned to love from a friend like you.

Add a New Animal

The hink of a new animal friend to put in this story. What things could you learn from that animal?

Draw a picture of your idea and write a sentence about it. You and your friends could put your pages together to make a new book!

Meet the
Author and Illustrator

Taro Gomi went to art school in Japan. Since then, he has drawn the pictures for over 100 children's books! Taro Gomi has done other jobs, too. He has worked on cartoons and he has drawn new ideas for children's clothes. He now lives in Japan with his wife and two daughters.

Meet More Animal Friends

Skip to My Lou
by Nadine Bernard Westcott
A farmer leaves his house,
and some animal friends
come to visit. Then the fun
begins!

Pretend You're a Cat
by Jean Marzollo
Can you purr like a cat? Find
out what the children in this
book can do.

Five Little Ducks

by Raffi

One by one, Mother Duck's children leave home. But when they come back, they have a nice surprise for Mother Duck!

A Children's Zoo

by Tana Hoban

What animal is striped black and white? The photographs in this book will help you name new animal friends.

Animal Mothers

by Atsushi Komori

Did you know that koala mothers carry their babies on their backs? This book is full of interesting information about animals and their mothers.

Read Alone Books

Are You My Baby?
Good Morning, Bears!
Let's Get a Pet

I can do it!

Big Book:
I Can't Get My Turtle to Move

The girl in this book can get all kinds of animals to do what she says. But when she tries to get a turtle to do things, it won't even move! Read this book together. Find out if the girl gets the turtle to move. Do you think she can do it?

You can do so many things! What did you do today that you couldn't do when you were a baby? What problems do you solve every day?

As you read these stories and poems, you will find out why each character might say, "I can do it!"

CONTENTS

I Wish I

Could Fly

written and illustrated by
Ron Maris

"Good morning, Bird.
I wish I could fly like you."

CRASH! BANG!
WALLOP! CRUNCH!

"Hello, Frog.

I wish I could dive like you."

FLOP!   PLOP!
SPLUTTER!   SPLASH!

"How are you, Squirrel?
I wish I could climb like you."

**WIBBLE! WOBBLE!
WRIGGLE! ROCK!**

"Good day, Rabbit.

I wish I could run like you."

**PUFF! PANT!
STAGGER! GASP!**

"I can't fly like Bird,

I can't dive like Frog,

I can't climb like Squirrel,

I can't run like Rabbit, but . . ."

"When it rains,
I don't get wet.
I'm **SNUG**, **WARM**,
COZY, and **DRY**!"

I wish I could...

Are you like Turtle? Do you wish you could fly like a bird? Or climb like a squirrel? Think of something you wish you could do.

Draw a picture of it. Talk about your picture with some friends.

I Speak, I Say, I Talk

 Cats purr.

 Lions roar.

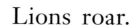 Owls hoot.

Bears snore.

 Crickets creak.

Mice squeak.

 Sheep baa.

But I SPEAK!

 Monkeys chatter.

Cows moo.

 Ducks quack.

Doves coo.

 Pigs squeal.

Horses neigh.

 Chickens cluck.

But I SAY!

Flies hum.

Dogs growl.

Bats screech.

Coyotes howl.

Frogs croak.

Parrots squawk.

Bees buzz.

But I TALK!

by Arnold L. Shapiro

MONSTER AND THE BABY

by Virginia Mueller
illustrated by Lynn Munsinger

Baby was crying.

Monster gave Baby one red block.

Baby cried.

Monster gave Baby two yellow blocks.

Baby cried.

Monster gave Baby three blue blocks.

Baby cried.

Monster put the three blue blocks on the bottom,

the two yellow blocks in the middle,

and the one red block on the top.

Monster hit the blocks!

Baby laughed and laughed.

Monster Can Do It!

If Monster had no blocks, do you think he could still find a way to make Baby laugh?

Think of a new way to get Baby to stop crying. Draw a picture of Monster doing something funny or nice for Baby. Add speech balloons to show what Monster and Baby are saying.

And So Can I!

BILL GILLHAM

This pig can peek over a fence . . .

and so can I!

This rabbit can wash her face . . .

and so can I!

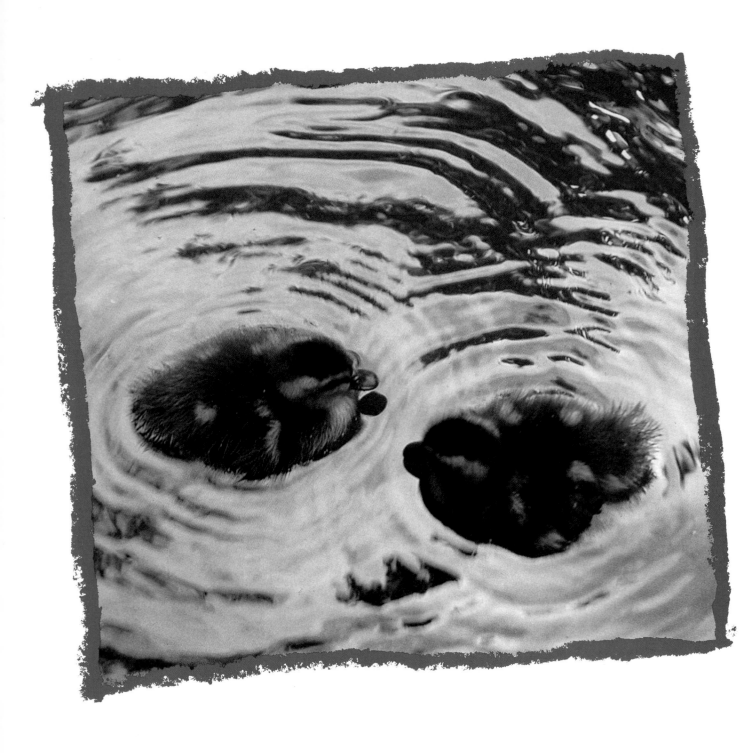

These little ducks can swim . . .

and so can I!

This donkey can eat an apple . . .

and so can I!

But none of them . . .

can read a book like me!

I Have a Very Special Book

by Hector Castro

translated from the Spanish

I have a very special book.

When I open it, beams of light come out.

When I read it, I think the world is different.

And that is why I love to read.

And that is why my book

Is very special to me!

BET YOU CAN'T

written and illustrated by
Penny Dale

147

148

154

157

Make a Game Book

The children in this story play a game to make cleaning up seem like fun. What kinds of games can you play?

Draw a picture of yourself playing your favorite game, and write a sentence about it. Put everyone's pages together and make a class game book. Then put your book in the games section of your school library.

Meet the Authors and Illustrators

Virginia Mueller has four children. When they were babies, her children liked to play with blocks. This gave Mrs. Mueller the idea for *Monster and the Baby*, her first story about Monster.

Virginia Mueller is still writing stories— but now she gets ideas from her six grandchildren!

Lynn Munsinger was born in Massachusetts and went to art school in Rhode Island. When she finished school, Ms. Munsinger began to draw pictures for children's books. One of her recent storybooks is *One Hungry Monster*. She has also drawn pictures for *Cricket*, a magazine for children.

Ron Maris has written many books about animals. He drew the pictures for all of his books, including *I Wish I Could Fly.*

When he is not writing, Mr. Maris likes to help people learn to draw. He is now an art teacher at a school in England.

Penny Dale went to art school in England. Later she worked in a theater making costumes and props for plays. She also drew the pictures for a book called *The Stopwatch.*

Penny Dale lives in Wales with her family.

More Books

**I Can't Get My
Turtle to Move**

by Elizabeth Lee O'Donnell
You have read this
counting book together.
Now read it again.
Can you count all the
animals that appear in
the story?

**The Chick and
the Duckling**

by Mirra Ginsburg
Each time the
duckling tries
something new, the
chick says, "Me too."
Will the chick change
its mind?

You Can Read

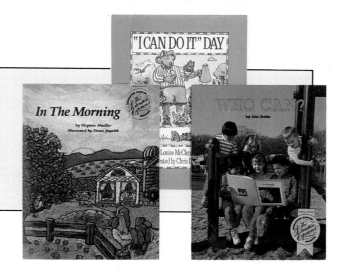

Molly Goes Hiking

by Ruth Radlauer
Molly wants to try out
her new backpack.
Follow her on a
hiking adventure.

Flap Your Wings and Try

by Charlotte Pomerantz
A baby bird learns to
fly — but how? Find
out what its secret is.

We Play

by Phyllis Hoffman
The children in this
book like to read,
dance, and cook at
school. Read about
what else they can do.

Max's Breakfast

by Rosemary Wells
Someone eats Max's
egg. Is it Max?

Acknowledgments

For each of the selections listed below, grateful acknowledgment is made for permission to excerpt and/or reprint original or copyrighted material, as follows:

Major Selections

"And So Can I!" by Bill Gillham. Copyright © 1987 by Bill Gillham, excerpts reprinted by permission of G.P. Putnam's Sons, and Methuen Children's Books.

Bet You Can't by Penny Dale. Copyright © 1988 by Penny Dale. Reprinted by permission of HarperCollins Publishers and Walker Books Ltd.

Dear Zoo by Rod Campbell. Copyright © 1982 by Rod Campbell. Reprinted by permission of Macmillan Publishing Company, and Campbell Books Ltd. (*Dear Zoo* is published as a flap book.)

I Wish I Could Fly by Ron Maris. Copyright © 1987 by Ron Maris. Reprinted by permission of Greenwillow Books (a division of William Morrow and Co.), and Julia MacRae Books.

Monster and the Baby, text copyright © 1985 by Virginia Mueller. Illustrations copyright © 1985 by Lynn Munsinger. Originally published in hardcover by Albert Whitman and Company. All rights reserved. Used with permission.

My Friends by Taro Gomi. Copyright © 1989 by Taro Gomi. English text copyright © 1990 by Chronicle Books. Reprinted by permission of Chronicle Books.

"On Our Way" by Eve Merriam from *Catch a Little Rhyme* by Eve Merriam. Copyright © 1966 by Eve Merriam. Reprinted by permission of Marian Reiner for the author.

"Together" from *Embrace: Selected Love Poems* by Paul Engle. Copyright © 1969 by Paul Engle. Reprinted by permission of Random House, Inc.

Who Is Tapping At My Window? by A. G. Deming, illustrated by Monica Wellington. Copyright © 1988 by Monica Wellington. Reprinted by permission of the publisher, Dutton Children's Books, a division of Penguin Books USA, Inc.

Poetry

"At the Zoo" from *Whispers and Other Poems*. Copyright © 1958 by Myra Cohn Livingston. Reprinted by permission of Marian Reiner for the author.

"Early Morning," a translation of a traditional Spanish poem, in *Tesoro de Poesía Juvenil: A Treasure of Poetry for Young People*, selected and edited by Maricarmen Ohara, Ph.D. Copyright © 1990 by Maricarmen Ohara. Published by Algeria Hispana Publications.

"I Have a Very Special Book" ("Un Libro Especial") by Hector Castro, in the MABE Anthology, 1989 Annual Conference. Copyright © 1989 by the Massachusetts Association for Bilingual Education. Reprinted by permission of the Massachusetts Association for Bilingual Education.

"I Speak, I Say, I Talk" by Arnold L. Shapiro from *Once Upon a Time*, Volume 1 of *Childcraft—The How and Why Library*. Copyright © 1989 World Book, Inc. By permission of the publisher.

"The Lost Cat" from *A Light in the Attic*, text and illustration by Shel Silverstein. Copyright © 1981 by Evil Eye Music, Inc. Reprinted by permission of Harper and Row, Publishers, Inc.

"Notice" from *One at a Time* by David McCord. Copyright © 1952 by David McCord. Reprinted by permission of Little, Brown and Company.

Credits

Program Design   Carbone Smolan Associates

Cover Design   Carbone Smolan Associates

Design   8–83 Carbone Smolan Associates;   84–165 Pronk & Associates

Introduction   (left to right) 1st row: Felicia Bond; Cecily Lang; Ajin;   2nd row: John Lei; Denise and Fernando; Felicia Bond;   3rd row: Felicia Bond; Ajin; John Lei;   4th row: John Lei; Ellen Sasaki; Felicia Bond

Table of Contents   4 Felicia Bond

Illustration   8–11 Ajin;   12–28 Monica Wellington;   29 Ajin;   30–35 Felicia Bond;   36–37 Denise and Fernando;   38–54 Rod Campbell;   55 Mary Lynn Blasutta;   56 Ajin;   57 Don Stuart;   58 Shel Silverstein;   59 Ellen Joy Sasaki;   60–79 Taro Gomi;   80 Cecily Lang;   81, 82–83 Ajin;   86 Pronk & Associates;   88–108 Ron Maris;   110–112 Julie Koontz;   113–126 Lynn Munsinger;   134 Yvette Banek;   135–159 Penny Dale;   162–163 Pronk & Associates

Photography   84 David Vance/The Image Bank (top left);   84–85 Rommel/Masterfile (top right);   84 Stephen Marks/Stockphotos, Inc. (bottom);   85 Andrew McKim/Masterfile (top right);   88–89 H. Armstrong Roberts/Miller Comstock

Assignment Photographers   Kenji Kerins   85 (bottom), 160–161, 164